CONTENTS

STAR WARS™

Pedigree®

Published 2012.
Pedigree Books Limited, Beech Hill House, Walnut Gardens, Exeter, Devon EX4 4DH
www.pedigreebooks.com | books@pedigreegroup.co.uk
The Pedigree trademark, email and website addresses, are the sole and exclusive properties
of Pedigree Group Limited, used under licence in this publication.

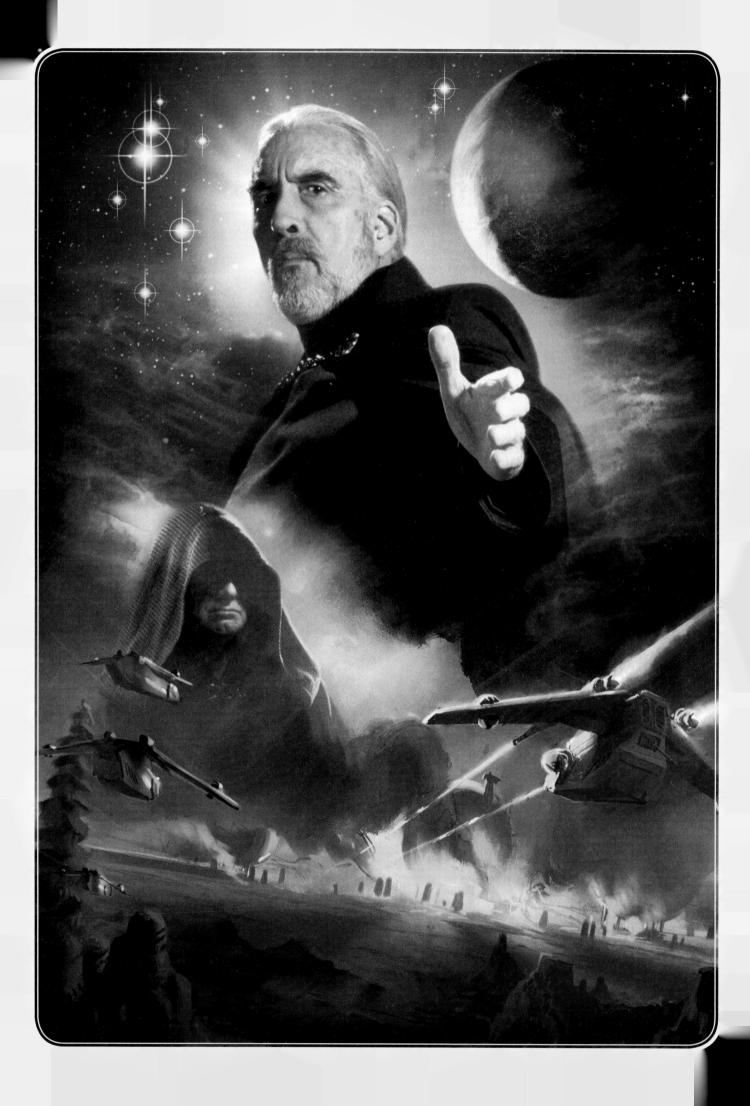

the skywalker family

ALTHOUGH COMING FROM HUMBLE BEGINNINGS, THE SKYWALKER FAMILY WAS DESTINED TO PLAY A VITAL ROLE IN THE FUTURE OF THE EMPIRE. AN ANCIENT JEDI PROPHECY TOLD OF A CHOSEN ONE WHO WOULD BRING BALANCE TO THE FORCE.

AS TIME PASSED, MORE AND MORE JEDI CAME TO BELIEVE THAT ANAKIN SKYWALKER WAS THE CHOSEN ONE.

SHMI

Shmi was sold into slavery as a young girl. She worked hard for her masters, never dreaming that her son would one day play an important part in galactic history.

When Jedi Master Qui-Gon Jinn arrived on Tatooine, Shmi was faced with an impossible decision. The Jedi saw great potential in her son, but for him to become a Padawan he would have to leave his home behind.

FACT FILE

NAME | Shmi Skywalker
HEIGHT | 1.63m
HAIR COLOUR | Brown
EYE COLOUR | Brown
HOME PLANET | Tatooine

Shmi wanted her son to have a better life so she agreed to let him go. She never stopped thinking about him, and they were briefly reunited when he rescued her from Tusken Raiders. However, she died in his arms. Taking a terrible revenge, Anakin slaughtered the whole Tusken clan.

Although his early life on Tatooine was hard, Anakin had great confidence in his abilities. As a young boy, he had the ability to build and repair anything. He was also a gifted pilot. When Qui-Gon Jinn met Anakin he saw that the Force was strong in him and believed him to be the Chosen One.

FACT FILE

NAME | Anakin Skywalker
HEIGHT | 1.85m
HAIR COLOUR | Light Brown
EYE COLOUR | Blue
HOME PLANET | Tatooine

The Jedi Council was sceptical, but Anakin proved his worth alongside his Master, Obi-Wan Kenobi. However, as he grew older, it became clear that the Jedi Council had reason to be concerned. Anakin could be arrogant and unpredictable, and often made impulsive, rebellious decisions. Some Jedi Masters believed that his training had begun too late.

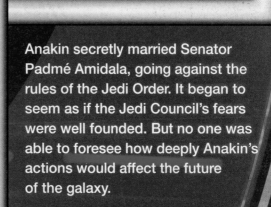

Anakin secretly married Senator Padmé Amidala, going against the rules of the Jedi Order. It began to seem as if the Jedi Council's fears were well founded. But no one was able to foresee how deeply Anakin's actions would affect the future of the galaxy.

THE PHANTOM MENACE

1

The galaxy was in chaos. A Trade Federation ship had blockaded the planet of Naboo, and two Jedi Knights were sent to try to settle the conflict.

2

When Obi-Wan and Qui-Gon realised that an invasion was planned, they hurried to warn the Queen of Naboo. They took along a clumsy Gungan called Jar Jar Binks.

3

Queen Amidala, the Jedi and Jar Jar escaped the planet and headed for Coruscant. On the way, they had to land on Tatooine due to a leaking hyperdrive.

4

Watto had the spare parts they needed, but they had no money.

5

Watto's kind-hearted slave boy, Anakin Skywalker, entered a Podrace and let Qui-Gon use the prize money to buy parts. The Force was very strong with Anakin, and it was clear to the Jedi that the boy was special.

6

The Sith Lord Darth Sidious ordered his apprentice Darth Maul to find Queen Amidala. Sidious was behind the blockade, and he wanted to cause trouble.

Qui-Gon set Anakin free and took him to Coruscant to train him as a Jedi. The Jedi Council said that the boy was too full of fear to become a Jedi, but Qui-Gon vowed to train Anakin himself.

The Supreme Chancellor could not help the Queen to fight the blockade, so she called for a vote of no confidence. Senator Palpatine was nominated as the new Supreme Chancellor, and the Queen returned to Naboo with Jar Jar, the Jedi and Anakin.

Queen Amidala made an alliance with the Gungans, and together the natives of Naboo fought the Trade Federation.

Meanwhile, Darth Maul arrived on the planet and fought the Jedi. Anakin hid inside the cockpit of a spare fighter, but it carried him up into space on autopilot!

While Anakin joined in the battle against the Trade Federation droid control ship in space, Darth Maul fatally wounded Qui-Gon Jinn. Obi-Wan killed the Sith apprentice and promised his dying Master that he would train Anakin.

Anakin and R2-D2 destroyed the droid control ship, and wiped out all the battle droids attacking the planet. Naboo was safe! But the Sith threat was lurking in the shadows, and there would be dark times ahead for the galaxy.

ODD ONE OUT

YOU ARE RESEARCHING DARTH MAUL IN THE JEDI ARCHIVES BUT ONE OF THE HOLOBOOKS IS FAULTY. IT SHOWS YOU NINE IMAGES OF DARTH MAUL BUT ONE IS INCORRECT... CAN YOU SPOT THE ODD ONE OUT?

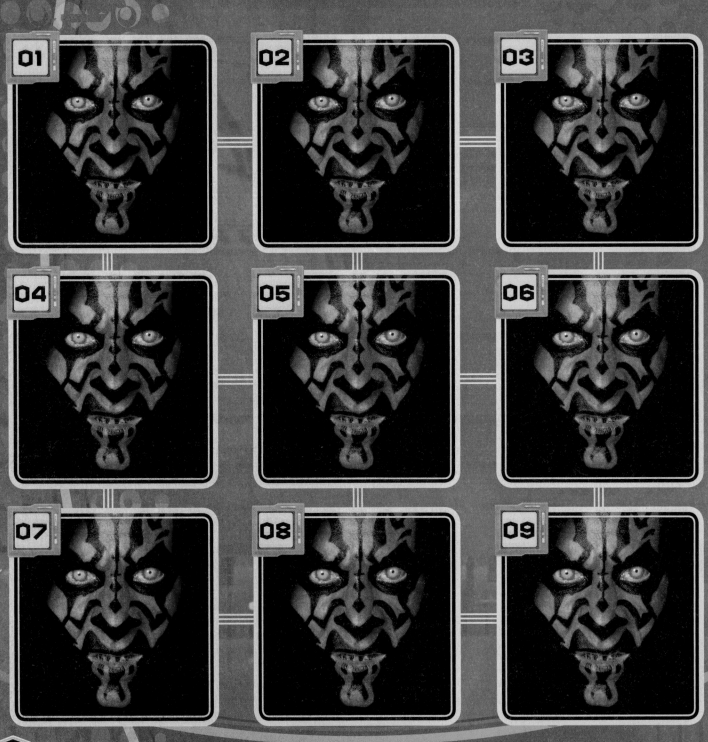

WORD WISDOM

CAN YOU MAKE SENSE OF THE SCRAMBLED WORDS BELOW? USE THE FORCE TO IDENTIFY THE WORDS BELOW AND TURN THEM INTO TWO PLANETS AND FOUR FAMOUS NAMES.

1 OBRNO

2 ARJ JRA INBSK

3 ATRDH AUML

4 NARINK KSEWYAKRL

5 ESATORN AANLPPTIE

6 NAOTTOIE

HOW TO DRAW
MACE WINDU

FOLLOW THESE STEPS TO
LEARN HOW TO DRAW
THE MAGICAL
MACE WINDU

PHASE
01

PHASE
02

Dex's Diner

DEX'S DINER WAS IN A RUN-DOWN INDUSTRIAL PARK AREA IN THE LOWER PART OF CORUSCANT. IT WAS A QUAINT, OLD-FASHIONED DINER THAT SERVED UP FRESHLY BREWED JAWA JUICE AND HOME-STYLE MEALS.

The streetwise, ingenious owner and cook, Dexter Jettster, was a four-armed Besalisk with a fascinating past. He had been a prospector at a mining system beyond the Outer Rim, manned rigs, run bars and brawled for a living. However, on Coruscant he valued his quiet life as a cook.

Dexter had renovated the old diner in a style that was nostalgic of the golden age of the Republic, with bright lights and tile floors. It looked simple, but it was clean and welcoming. The house specialities were fried nerfsteak and pickled gartro eggs, but diners could also get hold of valuable information. Dexter's experience and contacts meant that he was a source of vital information to those he trusted. He always kept his eyes and ears open, and his excellent memory enabled him to help his friends when they were seeking information.

When Dexter and Obi-Wan first met, the Besalisk was running a rough bar on the remote mining world of Ord Sigatt. He was using the bar as a front for supplying mercenaries and bounty hunters with guns. Eventually he sold his stock to Jango Fett and used the money to fund his trip to Coruscant.

After an assassination attempt on Senator Amidala, Obi-Wan went to Dexter in the hope that he would be able to identify the mysterious dart that had been used. Dexter knew about the Kaminoans through their cloning of miners and recognised it as a Kamino saberdart. Thanks to him, Obi-Wan was able to uncover the existence of the clone army.

COLOUR BY NUMBERS

THE ESCAPE OF COUNT DOOKU WITH THE PLANS FOR THE ULTIMATE WEAPON MARKED THE START OF THE CLONE WARS. USING THE COLOUR CODE, COMPLETE THE PICTURE OF THIS CRUCIAL MOMENT IN THE HISTORY OF THE REPUBLIC.

TOOLS OF THE TRADE

JANGO FETT

RETRACTABLE WRIST BLADES

DEADLY BOUNTY HUNTER JANGO FETT HAS AN ARSENAL OF WEAPONS AT HIS FINGERTIPS. CAN YOU SPOT THEM ALL? DRAW A LINE FROM THE LABELS BELOW TO THE ITEMS THAT THEY DESCRIBE

BLASTER RIFLE

DUAL BLASTER PISTOLS

SNARE ROCKET DARTS

FLAME PROJECTOR

VIBROBLADE

Jedi MASTER

THE RANK OF MASTER WAS THE HIGHEST STATUS OF THE JEDI ORDER. TO PROGRESS FROM PADAWAN TO JEDI MASTER USUALLY TOOK DECADES, AND MANY NEVER ACHIEVED THIS PINNACLE.

To become a Jedi Master took patience, inner strength, wisdom and a deep connection to the Force. A Jedi also had to have trained a student to completion. It was very important that they should be able to pass on their hard-earned skills by teaching a new generation of Jedi. A Jedi was allowed only one Padawan at a time, and the training could last for many years

There were no ranks among Jedi Masters, but the most highly respected of them were invited to sit upon the Jedi Council. These individuals used their wisdom and experience to instruct others in the ways of the Force and preserve peace in the galaxy.

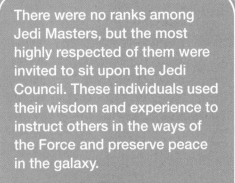

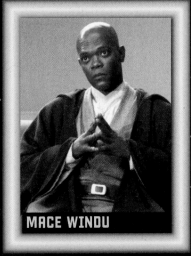

MACE WINDU

EVEN PIELL

PLO KOON

KI-ADI-MUNDI

JEDI COUNCIL

It was also the role of the Jedi Council to seek out Force-sensitive children across the galaxy and offer them instruction in the Jedi Order.

There were some Jedi Masters who were known as scholars and were sometimes called Jedi Sage Masters. They were the keepers of knowledge, and they spent much of their time in research or meditation. If a question or problem arose that could not be answered by members of the Jedi Council, these Sage Masters were consulted.

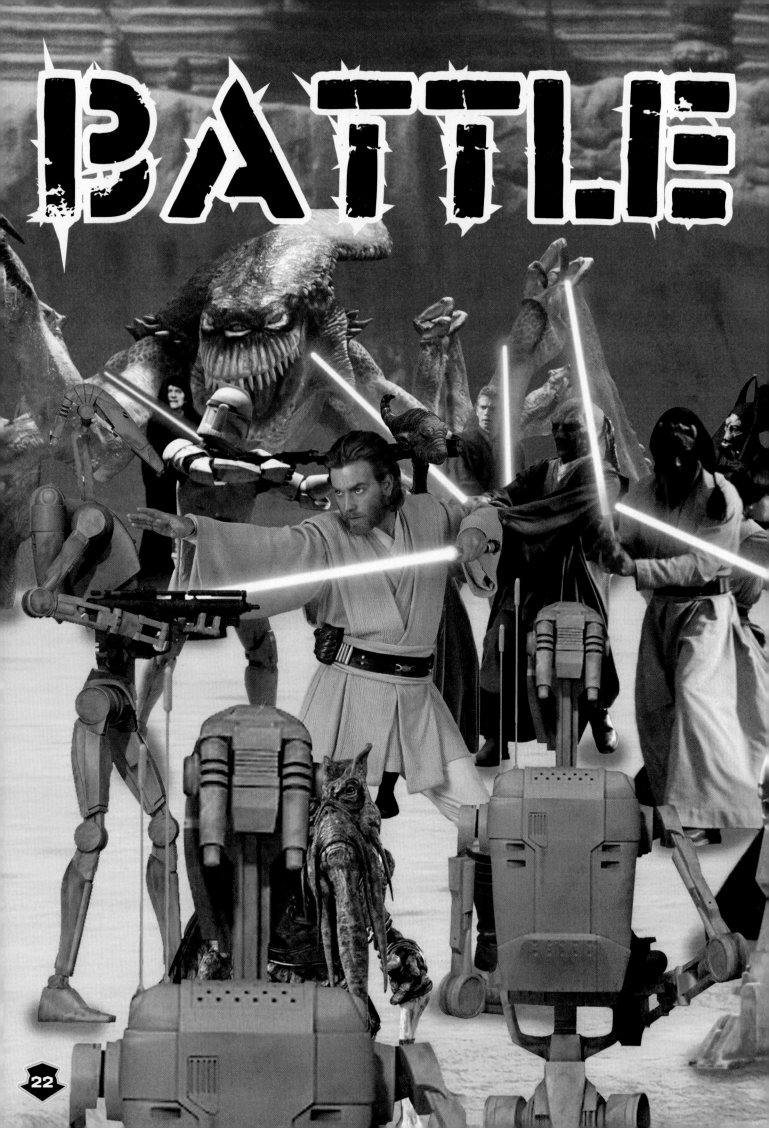

BATTLE

CHALLENGE

CAN YOU FIND SIX SEPARATIST LEADERS
HIDDEN IN THIS DRAMATIC BATTLE?

23

Attack OF THE Clones

THERE WAS UNREST IN THE GALACTIC SENATE. THE REPUBLIC WAS BEING THREATENED BY THE SEPARATIST MOVEMENT, LED BY A RUTHLESS FORMER JEDI CALLED COUNT DOOKU. MORE AND MORE STAR SYSTEMS WERE JOINING THE SEPARATISTS. THE JEDI STRUGGLED TO SECURE ORDER IN THE GALAXY, BUT THEY WERE OVERWHELMED.

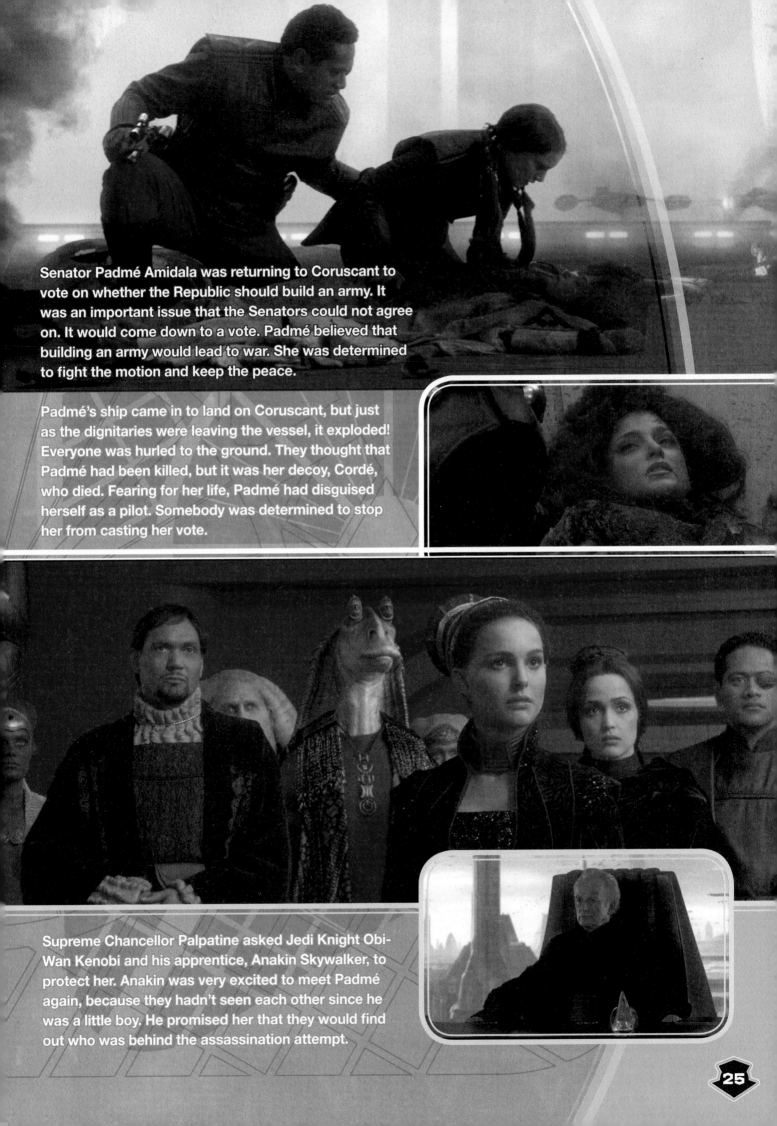

Senator Padmé Amidala was returning to Coruscant to vote on whether the Republic should build an army. It was an important issue that the Senators could not agree on. It would come down to a vote. Padmé believed that building an army would lead to war. She was determined to fight the motion and keep the peace.

Padmé's ship came in to land on Coruscant, but just as the dignitaries were leaving the vessel, it exploded! Everyone was hurled to the ground. They thought that Padmé had been killed, but it was her decoy, Cordé, who died. Fearing for her life, Padmé had disguised herself as a pilot. Somebody was determined to stop her from casting her vote.

Supreme Chancellor Palpatine asked Jedi Knight Obi-Wan Kenobi and his apprentice, Anakin Skywalker, to protect her. Anakin was very excited to meet Padmé again, because they hadn't seen each other since he was a little boy. He promised her that they would find out who was behind the assassination attempt.

25

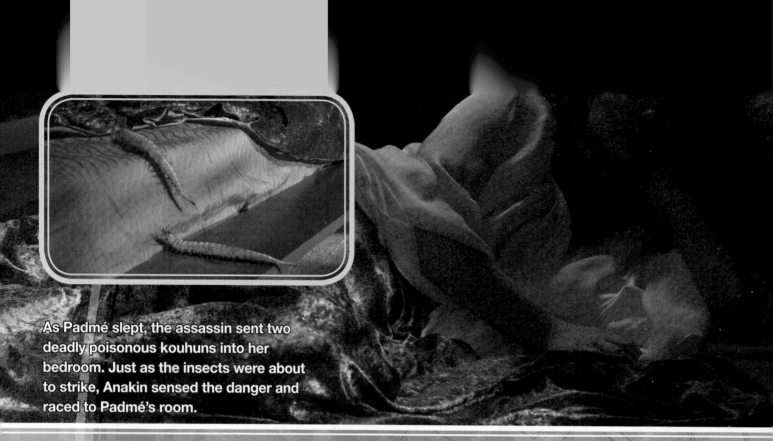

As Padmé slept, the assassin sent two deadly poisonous kouhuns into her bedroom. Just as the insects were about to strike, Anakin sensed the danger and raced to Padmé's room.

Obi-Wan and Anakin chased the assassin through the city. They caught her, but just as she was about to tell them who was behind the assassination attempt, she dropped down dead. She had been shot by a saberdart, fired by a mysterious armoured rocket man. Who wanted Padmé dead?

Obi-Wan set out to investigate, leaving Anakin to protect Padmé. The Jedi Council decided that Padmé would be safer back on her home planet of Naboo. Anakin was ordered to take her there, and soon realised that he was falling in love with her.

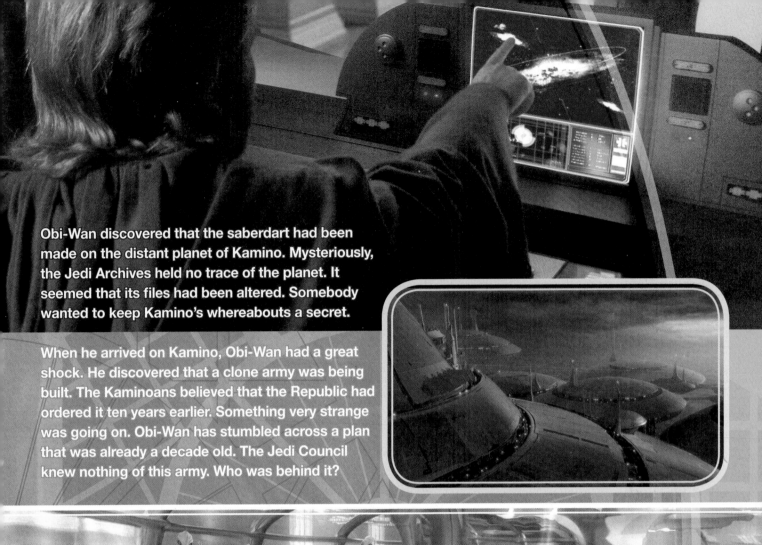

Obi-Wan discovered that the saberdart had been made on the distant planet of Kamino. Mysteriously, the Jedi Archives held no trace of the planet. It seemed that its files had been altered. Somebody wanted to keep Kamino's whereabouts a secret.

When he arrived on Kamino, Obi-Wan had a great shock. He discovered that a clone army was being built. The Kaminoans believed that the Republic had ordered it ten years earlier. Something very strange was going on. Obi-Wan has stumbled across a plan that was already a decade old. The Jedi Council knew nothing of this army. Who was behind it?

Obi-Wan met a bounty hunter called Jango Fett. He had been hired as the template for the clones. Obi-Wan believed that Jango was the assassin he was looking for. He reported back to the Jedi Council, and Yoda instructed him to take Jango into custody for questioning.

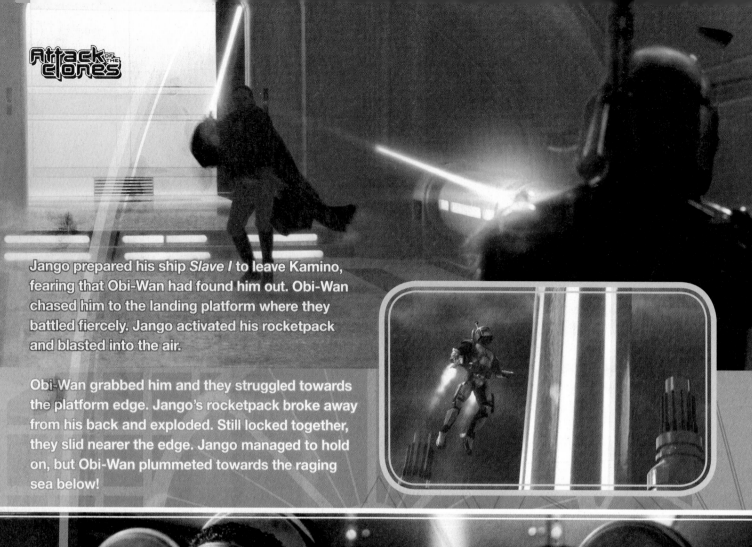

Jango prepared his ship *Slave I* to leave Kamino, fearing that Obi-Wan had found him out. Obi-Wan chased him to the landing platform where they battled fiercely. Jango activated his rocketpack and blasted into the air.

Obi-Wan grabbed him and they struggled towards the platform edge. Jango's rocketpack broke away from his back and exploded. Still locked together, they slid nearer the edge. Jango managed to hold on, but Obi-Wan plummeted towards the raging sea below!

Believing that Obi-Wan was dead, Jango left Kamino with his son Boba. But it wasn't easy to kill a Jedi. Obi-Wan used the Force to save himself, and was just in time to place a homing device on Jango's ship. He followed it to the planet of Geonosis.

Meanwhile, Anakin had been having nightmares that his mother was in terrible danger on Tatooine. He could sense her pain and suffering, and he couldn't bear it. He told Padmé that he had to go to Tatooine to find his mother. Padmé felt a powerful connection to the young Jedi, and decided to go with him.

On Tatooine, they discovered that Anakin's mother had been kidnapped by the ruthless Tusken Raiders. Everyone had given her up for dead, but Anakin knew that she was still alive. He would not give up hope. Driven by his love, he searched the desert until he found the Tusken camp.

Shmi Skywalker was badly hurt. She was clinging on to life by a thread, but she still recognised her beloved son. They embraced, but then she died in his arms. Anakin could not contain his pain and anger. He let them overpower him, and took a terrible revenge on the Tusken Raiders. He slaughtered every single one of them.

On Geonosis, Obi-Wan found that the planet's huge underground factories were assembling thousands of battle droids. That could mean only one thing – the Separatist movement was preparing for war.

Obi-Wan overheard a meeting between Count Dooku and the leaders of the Separatist movement. Their droid army was almost complete.

Obi-Wan had to tell the Jedi Council what he had heard. He started to transmit his message to Anakin, asking him to send it on to the Council. However, droidekas were rapidly closing in on him. Obi-Wan was captured before he could finish his report.

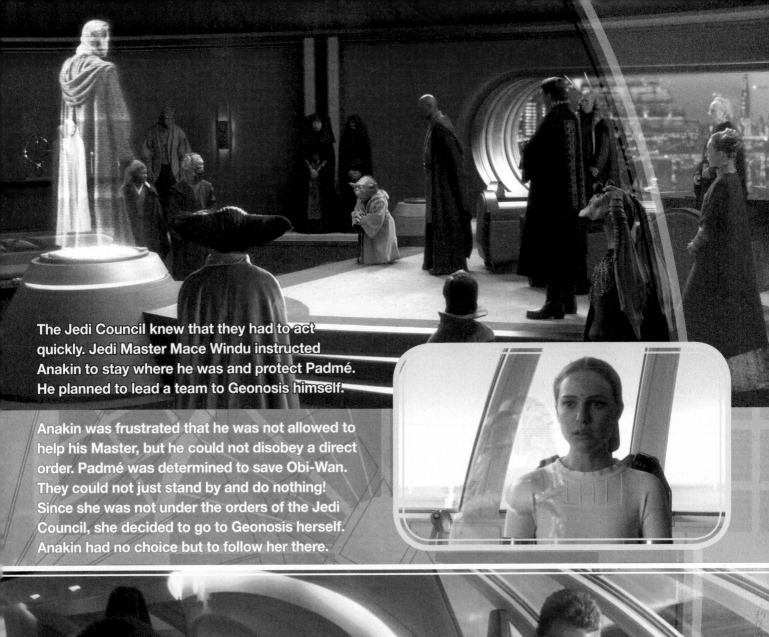

The Jedi Council knew that they had to act quickly. Jedi Master Mace Windu instructed Anakin to stay where he was and protect Padmé. He planned to lead a team to Geonosis himself.

Anakin was frustrated that he was not allowed to help his Master, but he could not disobey a direct order. Padmé was determined to save Obi-Wan. They could not just stand by and do nothing! Since she was not under the orders of the Jedi Council, she decided to go to Geonosis herself. Anakin had no choice but to follow her there.

On Coruscant, there was a sense of panic in the Senate. The Jedi were not strong enough in numbers to fight a droid army. It was agreed to grant Chancellor Palpatine emergency powers, which would allow him to govern without the delays usually caused by the Senate voting. This enabled him to call the clone army into battle.

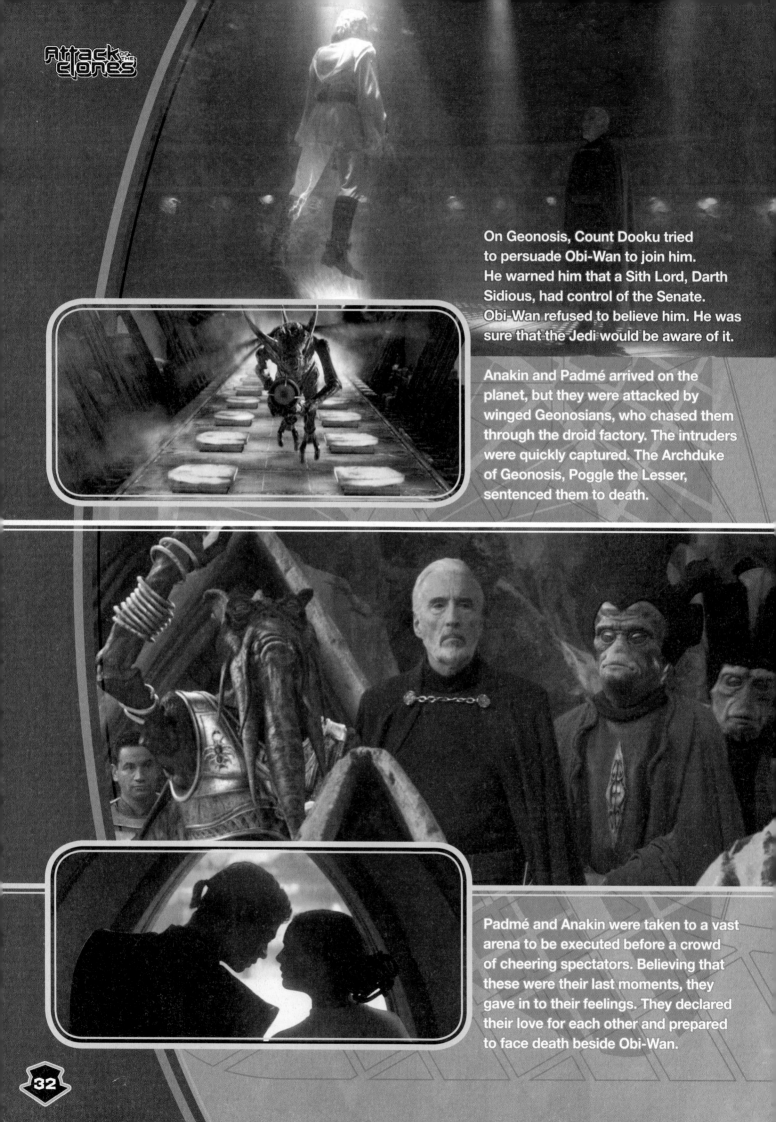

On Geonosis, Count Dooku tried to persuade Obi-Wan to join him. He warned him that a Sith Lord, Darth Sidious, had control of the Senate. Obi-Wan refused to believe him. He was sure that the Jedi would be aware of it.

Anakin and Padmé arrived on the planet, but they were attacked by winged Geonosians, who chased them through the droid factory. The intruders were quickly captured. The Archduke of Geonosis, Poggle the Lesser, sentenced them to death.

Padmé and Anakin were taken to a vast arena to be executed before a crowd of cheering spectators. Believing that these were their last moments, they gave in to their feelings. They declared their love for each other and prepared to face death beside Obi-Wan.

Attack of the Clones

While the crowd roared for blood, Anakin, Padmé and Obi-Wan were chained to pillars and left to await their fate. Giant monsters rampaged into the stadium, ready to attack. Padmé managed to free herself from her chains, and Anakin and Obi-Wan had to use all their Jedi skills to save themselves.

The three friends battled for their lives. Anakin rode one of the monsters in front of the crowd and Padmé jumped up behind him. Incredibly, they began to gain the upper hand, but still there was no way of escaping from the stadium. The Separatist leaders were furious and sent in the droidekas to finish them off once and for all.

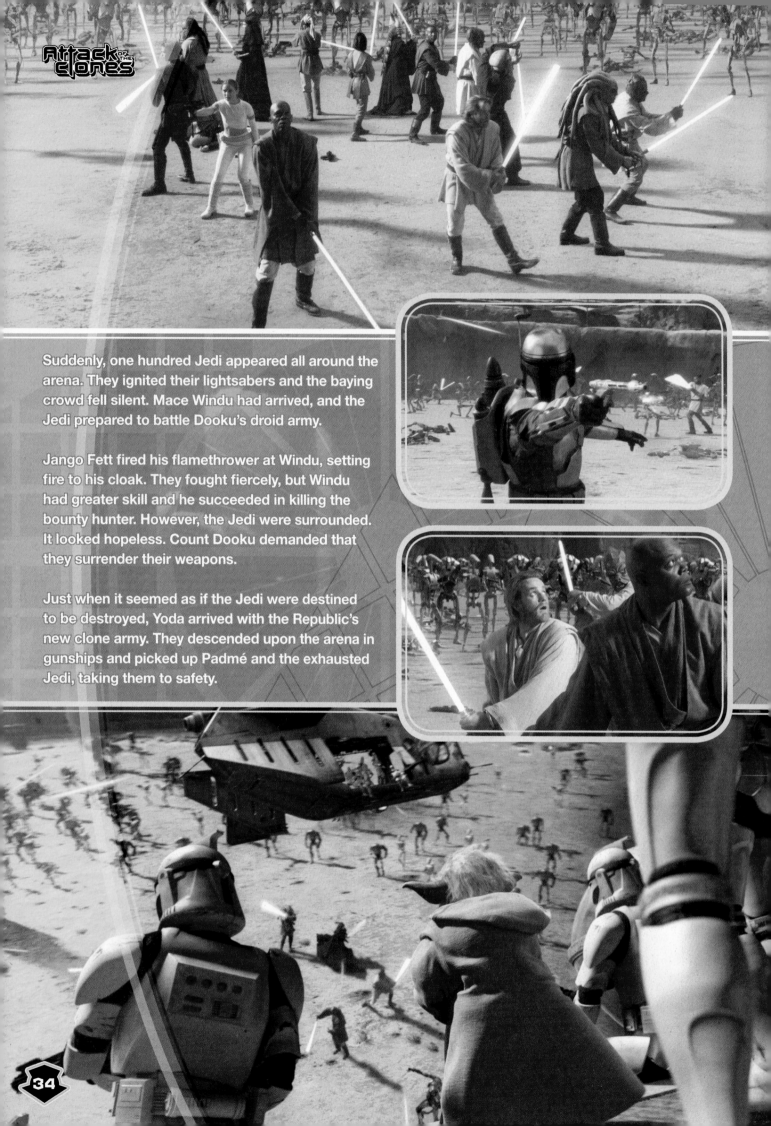

Suddenly, one hundred Jedi appeared all around the arena. They ignited their lightsabers and the baying crowd fell silent. Mace Windu had arrived, and the Jedi prepared to battle Dooku's droid army.

Jango Fett fired his flamethrower at Windu, setting fire to his cloak. They fought fiercely, but Windu had greater skill and he succeeded in killing the bounty hunter. However, the Jedi were surrounded. It looked hopeless. Count Dooku demanded that they surrender their weapons.

Just when it seemed as if the Jedi were destined to be destroyed, Yoda arrived with the Republic's new clone army. They descended upon the arena in gunships and picked up Padmé and the exhausted Jedi, taking them to safety.

Outside the arena, a much larger battle was in the making. The Republic's clone army surrounded the droid army of the Separatists. Panic broke out among the Separatist leaders. They ordered their forces to retreat, and starships begin to take off. Nute Gunray escaped while Poggle the Lesser entrusted Count Dooku with the plans for the ultimate weapon.

The Trade Federation droid control ship burst into a giant fireball under heavy fire from the clone forces. Yoda instructed his troops to capture Dooku, who sped away as he was chased by Obi-Wan and Anakin. He had to be stopped!

Obi-Wan and Anakin caught up with Count Dooku. Anakin was wild with anger and ignored his Master's orders. He charged rashly at the ex-Jedi. Dooku smiled calmly and unleashed a blast of Force lightning. Anakin was thrown across the room and lay very still.

Obi-Wan stayed calm and engaged Dooku in combat, but Dooku was a master swordsman. He had years of experience and a great deal of skill, and this gave him the edge.

Obi-Wan found it hard to defend himself. Dooku injured Obi-Wan in the shoulder and the thigh, weakening him and sending him crashing to the floor. Obi-Wan's lightsaber slid out of reach and he was defenceless.

Dooku's lightsaber flashed down on Obi-Wan . . . and struck Anakin's blade.

Anakin fearlessly stared into the eyes of the Sith Lord and used all his strength to force Dooku back. Obi-Wan threw Anakin his lightsaber and the young Padawan attacked with both blades. Still he was not strong enough.

Dooku drove him backwards against the wall. Then, with a terrible sweep of his blade, he cut Anakin's arm off at the elbow. Anakin dropped to the ground in agony and Count Dooku raised his lightsaber to deliver the final blow.

Suddenly, Yoda appeared out of the smoke. Dooku turned away from Anakin and mockingly greeted his old Master.

He used the Force to hurl huge boulders at Yoda, but the wise old Jedi avoided them effortlessly. A mighty duel began. Dooku sent Force lightning flashing through the air, but Yoda used the Force to deflect it.

They were both skilled warriors and it was a close battle. At first, Dooku attacked while Yoda parried every thrust. Then Dooku began to tire, and that was when Yoda attacked. He flew through the air, swinging his lightsaber. His swordplay was so fast that the blade became a blur of light. Dooku was forced backwards.

Dooku quickly realised that he could not defeat Yoda. Sooner or later he would be struck down. Desperately he searched the hanger for a way to escape. His eyes settled on a large crane. This was his one chance! With a mighty effort he used the Force to topple the crane, which fell towards Obi-Wan and Anakin.

Yoda closed his eyes and concentrated. He used the Force to stop the crane from crushing his injured friends. His focus was immense, but he could not duel at the same time. He chose to save his friends and let his enemy go. Count Dooku ran to his ship and made his escape. The exhausted Jedi struggled to their feet but it was too late. Dooku's ship rose into the sky and whisked him away.

Count Dooku landed his solar
sailer on a secret landing platform
in a deserted, burned-out area of
Coruscant. Waiting for him was
the sinister hooded figure of Darth
Sidious. Dooku eagerly gave him the
news he had been waiting for: the
war had begun. Darth Sidious smiled.
Everything was working out exactly as
he had planned.

Meanwhile, the Jedi Council was
worried. They could not celebrate the
victory of the battle; they could only
mourn the beginning of a war.

Anakin, fitted with a new
mechanical arm, escorted
Padmé back to Naboo.
There they held a wedding
ceremony with just C-3PO
and R2-D2 as witnesses.
It would have to be kept a
secret, for the Jedi were not
supposed to marry.

The Clone Wars had started,
and no one could know what
the future would hold. One
thing was certain – there
were darker times ahead.

SHADOW SEARCHER

HOW STRONG ARE YOUR POWERS OF OBSERVATION?
CAN YOU RECOGNISE YOUR FRIENDS AND ENEMIES
EVEN IN THE DARK?

JEDI PROPHECY

THIS PROPHECY HAS BEEN FOUND IN THE JEDI ARCHIVES. IT CONTAINS IMPORTANT INFORMATION ABOUT THE SEPARATISTS,

BUT IT HAS BEEN DAMAGED. CAN YOU FILL IN THE MISSING WORDS AND HELP OBI-WAN?

Senator Padmé ▓▓▓▓ is in danger! An attempt will be made on her life. The ▓▓▓▓ will tell you nothing, but a clue could lead you to the ocean planet of ▓▓▓▓. There you will find a secret ▓▓▓ hidden by the Republic.

There are challenges ahead, young Jedi. Your quest will lead you to the desert planet of ▓▓▓▓ where you will find great danger awaits you! A former ▓▓▓ will try to tempt you. You must remain strong. The Jedi Council must be told of the ▓▓▓▓ ▓▓▓ before it is too late.

GO NOW, YOUNG JEDI, AND DO YOUR DUTY.

GEONOSIS » KAMINO ARMY » AMIDALA » JEDI » ASSASSIN » DROID ARMY

Weddings

THE JEDI WERE FORBIDDEN FROM FORMING ATTACHMENTS OR HAVING POSSESSIONS BECAUSE THEY WERE SEEN AS A DISTRACTION FROM THE JEDI'S FOCUS ON THE FORCE.

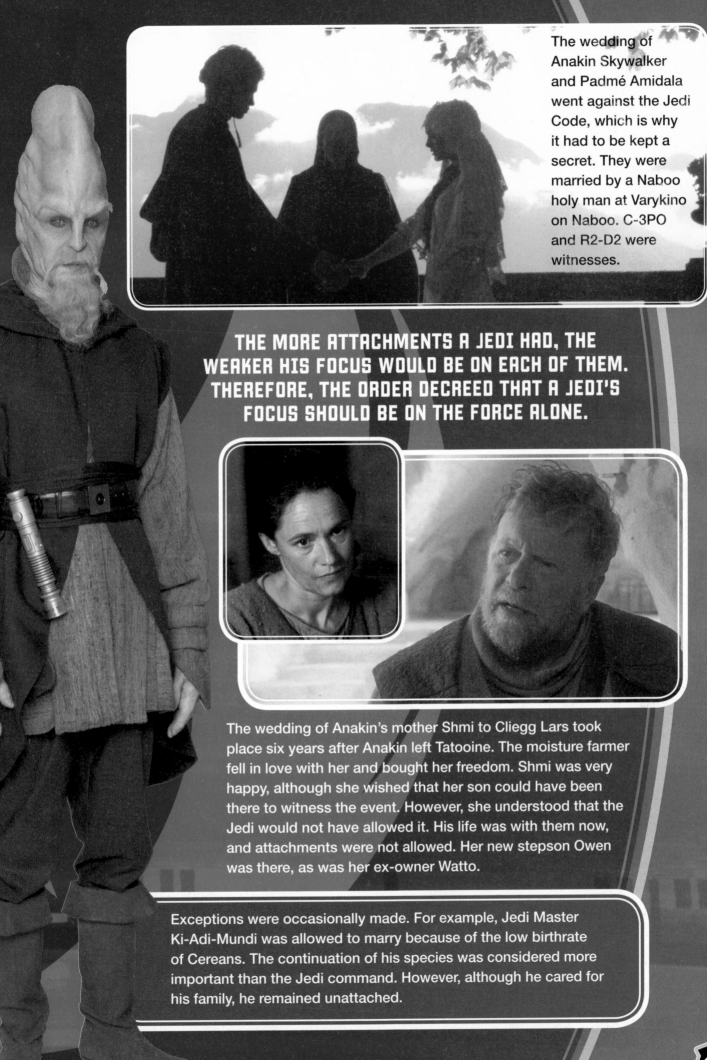

The wedding of Anakin Skywalker and Padmé Amidala went against the Jedi Code, which is why it had to be kept a secret. They were married by a Naboo holy man at Varykino on Naboo. C-3PO and R2-D2 were witnesses.

THE MORE ATTACHMENTS A JEDI HAD, THE WEAKER HIS FOCUS WOULD BE ON EACH OF THEM. THEREFORE, THE ORDER DECREED THAT A JEDI'S FOCUS SHOULD BE ON THE FORCE ALONE.

The wedding of Anakin's mother Shmi to Cliegg Lars took place six years after Anakin left Tatooine. The moisture farmer fell in love with her and bought her freedom. Shmi was very happy, although she wished that her son could have been there to witness the event. However, she understood that the Jedi would not have allowed it. His life was with them now, and attachments were not allowed. Her new stepson Owen was there, as was her ex-owner Watto.

Exceptions were occasionally made. For example, Jedi Master Ki-Adi-Mundi was allowed to marry because of the low birthrate of Cereans. The continuation of his species was considered more important than the Jedi command. However, although he cared for his family, he remained unattached.

Poggle's

A BOARD GAME FOR TWO OR MORE PLAYERS

MAKE YOUR WAY ACROSS THE GALAXY AND HUNT DOWN YOUR PREY.

1. THROW THE DICE TO DECIDE WHO WILL GO FIRST. THE HIGHEST SCORER STARTS THE GAME.

2. THROW YOUR DICE AND MOVE YOUR MARKER ALONG THE CORRECT NUMBER OF SPACES.

3. THE FIRST BOUNTY HUNTER TO REACH GEONOSIS IS THE WINNER! REMEMBER, YOU MUST THROW EXACTLY THE RIGHT NUMBER TO WIN THE GAME.

START	1 >	2 >	3 >
< 18	< 17	< 16	YOU SNEAK ON BOARD A DIPLOMATIC YACHT. MOVE FORWARD TWO SPACES. / < 14
19 >	YOU TAIL YOUR PREY TO A WAREHOUSE IN CORUSCANT. SWAP MARKER POSITIONS WITH THE PLAYER ON YOUR RIGHT.	21 >	22 > / 23 >
< 38	< 37	< 36	YOU ARE BETRAYED BY ANOTHER BOUNTY HUNTER. RETURN TO THE START. / < 34
39 >	YOU TRAP ANAKIN SKYWALKER ON TATOOINE. TAKE ANOTHER TURN.	41 >	42 > / 43 >
	FINISH	< 55	< 54

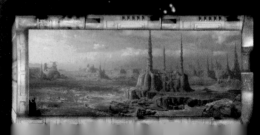

Minions

YOU AND YOUR FELLOW PLAYERS ARE BOUNTY HUNTERS EMPLOYED BY ARCHDUKE POGGLE THE LESSER TO DESTROY HIS ENEMIES.

YOU WILL NEED DICE AND A MARKER FOR EACH PLAYER.

4>

YOU TRAP ANAKIN SKYWALKER ON TATOOINE. TAKE ANOTHER TURN.

6>

7>

8>

<13

<12

<11

YOU STRIKE A DEAL WITH DARTH SIDIOUS. MOVE FORWARD THREE SPACES.

<9

24>

YOU ARE STRANDED ON A DESERT PLANET. MISS A TURN.

26>

27>

28>

<33

<32

<31

YOU LOSE ONE OF YOUR PRISONERS. MOVE BACK FOUR SPACES.

<29

44>

YOU TAIL YOUR PREY TO A WAREHOUSE IN CORUSCANT. SWAP MARKER POSITIONS WITH THE PLAYER ON YOUR RIGHT.

46>

47>

48>

<53

<52

<51

YOU STRIKE A DEAL WITH DARTH SIDIOUS. MOVE FORWARD THREE SPACES.

<49

SEPARATISTS

THE SEPARATIST MOVEMENT WAS FORMED BY A COLLECTION OF SOLAR SYSTEMS WHOSE GOVERNMENTS WISHED TO LEAVE THE REPUBLIC.

Since these governments did not have their own army, they made an alliance with the Commerce Guilds and the Trade Federation.

The rebellious solar systems felt that the Republic had become weak, due to corruption and bureaucracy. In some parts of the galaxy, especially outlying systems, heavy taxes were paid but no improvements were seen.

Count Dooku took advantage of this discontent, hoping to bring about radical change. In two short years, he had a following of several thousand solar systems.

The threat became more and more serious, and the Jedi began to fear that this would lead to open war.

Violent situations started to break out across the galaxy, and there were not enough Jedi to keep the peace. They were stretched too thin, and some worried senators started to call for the creation of an army to deal with the problems. Others, including Padmé Amidala, believed that this would start a civil war.

No one realised that the Separatists were already preparing for war. Count Dooku promised institutions like the Corporate Alliance, the Trade Federation and the Commerce Guild that the new order would work in their favour. In return, these institutions promised their massive droid armies to Dooku's cause. This agreement was called the Confederacy of Independent Systems.

The Republic launched an attack on the Separatists, using a clone army that they had just discovered they owned. This battle marked the beginning of the Clone Wars.

DARTH SIDIOUS HAD SPENT YEARS PLANNING HOW TO DESTROY THE JEDI AND RULE THE GALAXY, AND HE USED THE SEPARATIST LEADERS WITHOUT MERCY.

Revenge of the Sith

1 After three years of war, General Grievous kidnapped Chancellor Palpatine. Obi-Wan and Anakin were sent to rescue him from General Grievous's ship, but Count Dooku was determined to stop them. A mighty duel began.

2 Obi-Wan was knocked out, but Anakin disarmed Count Dooku and cut off his hands. Palpatine encouraged his passion and anger, and Anakin ignored the Jedi Code and cut off Count Dooku's head. In the confusion, General Grievous escaped.

3 Anakin's secret wife, Padmé, was pregnant, and Anakin was having nightmares that she would die while giving birth. When Palpatine told Anakin that the Sith had discovered how to stop death, Anakin was intrigued. More than anything, he wanted to save Padmé.

4 Palpatine drove a wedge between Anakin and his Jedi Masters. The Jedi didn't trust the Chancellor, but Anakin believed in him. However, while Obi-Wan was away finding and destroying General Grievous, Anakin learned that Palpatine was really Darth Sidious. He rushed to tell the Jedi Council the terrible truth.

5 As Mace Windu and Palpatine duelled, Anakin realised that Palpatine was his only chance of saving Padmé.

6 He cut off Mace's hand to stop him from killing the Chancellor. When Palpatine killed Mace, Anakin turned to the dark side.

The Chancellor gave an order for all Jedi to be obliterated. Anakin, obeying the Chancellor's orders, went to the Jedi Temple to destroy everyone there – including the younglings. Then he went to Mustafar to cut down the Separatists while Palpatine reorganised the Republic into the first Galactic Empire.

Padmé rushed to her husband's side on Mustafar. She didn't know that he had turned to the dark side, or that Obi-Wan was hiding on her ship. When Anakin saw Obi-Wan, he assumed that Padmé had betrayed him. He half choked her and she fell to the ground.

On Coruscant, Master Yoda duelled with Palpatine but was defeated. The Republic and the Jedi Order had been destroyed.

It broke Obi-Wan's heart to fight the boy he had trained. But he did not believe that there was still good in Anakin. He cut off Anakin's limbs and left him to burn in Mustafar's boiling lava.

Padmé was heartbroken, and she lost the will to live. But before she died, she gave birth to twins called Luke and Leia. Yoda went into hiding, Bail Organa adopted Leia, and Obi-Wan took Luke to live with his uncle on Tatooine.

Palpatine saved Anakin's life, and enclosed his broken body in the black armour of Darth Vader. When Anakin found out that Padmé was dead, he was filled with anger and despair. For the next nineteen years, his rage would rule his life.

JEDI TEACHER

USE THE GRID TO COPY THIS PICTURE OF A WISE JEDI TEACHER. THEN FILL IN HIS NAME BELOW YOUR DRAWING.

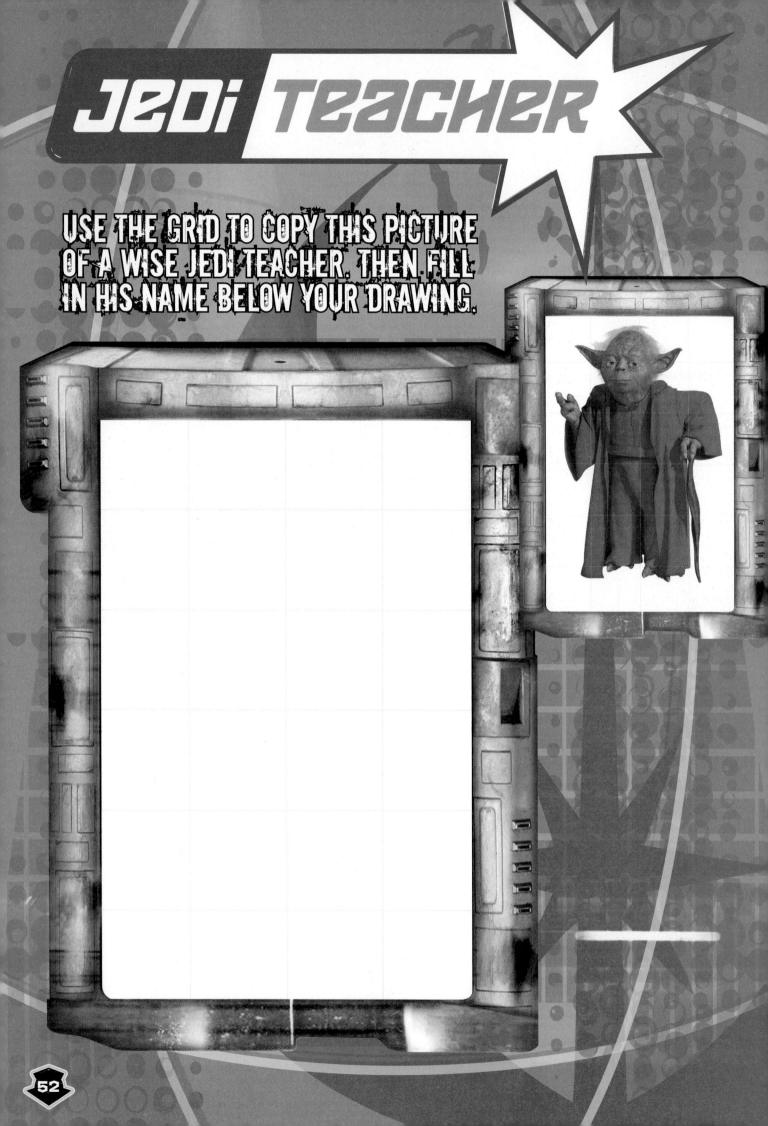

SUDOKU CHALLENGE

TO BECOME A JEDI YOU MUST OVERCOME MANY CHALLENGES. TEST YOUR MENTAL POWERS AND COMPLETE THIS SUDOKU PUZZLE.

EVERY LINE, COLUMN AND MINI-GRID MUST CONTAIN THE NUMBERS 1 TO 9.

	7			6			2	
	3	2	9	7	5			
	6	5		4	3			
6	8					7	1	
1	7				9		5	
9	5				2	8		
	4	8	2	1				
	1	3	5	6	4			
5			1			3		

MIGHTY MONSTERS
OF GEONOSIS

GEONOSIS IS INFAMOUS FOR ITS EXECUTION ARENA. ANAKIN, PADMÉ AND OBI-WAN ONCE FOUND THEMSELVES FACING TERRIFYING MONSTERS BEFORE A CHEERING CROWD.

CAN YOU DESIGN A GIANT MONSTER FIT FOR THE GEONOSIAN ARENA REMEMBER, IT MUST BE A CHALLENGE EVEN FOR THE BRAVEST JEDI KNIGHTS. WHEN YOU HAVE DRAWN AND COLOURED IN YOUR MONSTER, WRITE ITS NAME BENEATH YOUR PICTURE.

Fact or Fiction

LOOK AT THESE STATEMENTS. SOME OF THEM ARE TRUE BUT SOME ARE FALSEHOODS, DESIGNED TO UNDERMINE THE REPUBLIC. CAN YOU PICK FACT FROM FICTION?

1 PADMÉ AMIDALA CAME FROM THE PLANET GEONOSIS.

2 POGGLE THE LESSER WAS ARCHDUKE OF GEONOSIS.

3 JANGO FETT WAS KILLED BY OBI-WAN KENOBI.

4 COUNT DOOKU WAS ONCE A JEDI MASTER.

5 ANAKIN SKYWALKER SPENT HIS EARLY YEARS AS A SLAVE ON THE PLANET OF TATOOINE.

6 COUNT DOOKU ESCAPED THE JEDI WITH THE PLANS FOR THE ULTIMATE WEAPON.

7 ANAKIN SKYWALKER'S MOTHER DIED WHEN HE WAS A BABY.

8 SENATOR PADMÉ AMIDALA SECRETLY MARRIED ANAKIN SKYWALKER.

9 MACE WINDU BATTLED BOUNTY HUNTER JANGO FETT ON THE PLANET OF KAMINO.

10 THE SEPARATISTS BUILT A CLONE ARMY AND PLANNED TO ATTACK THE REPUBLIC.

CLONING

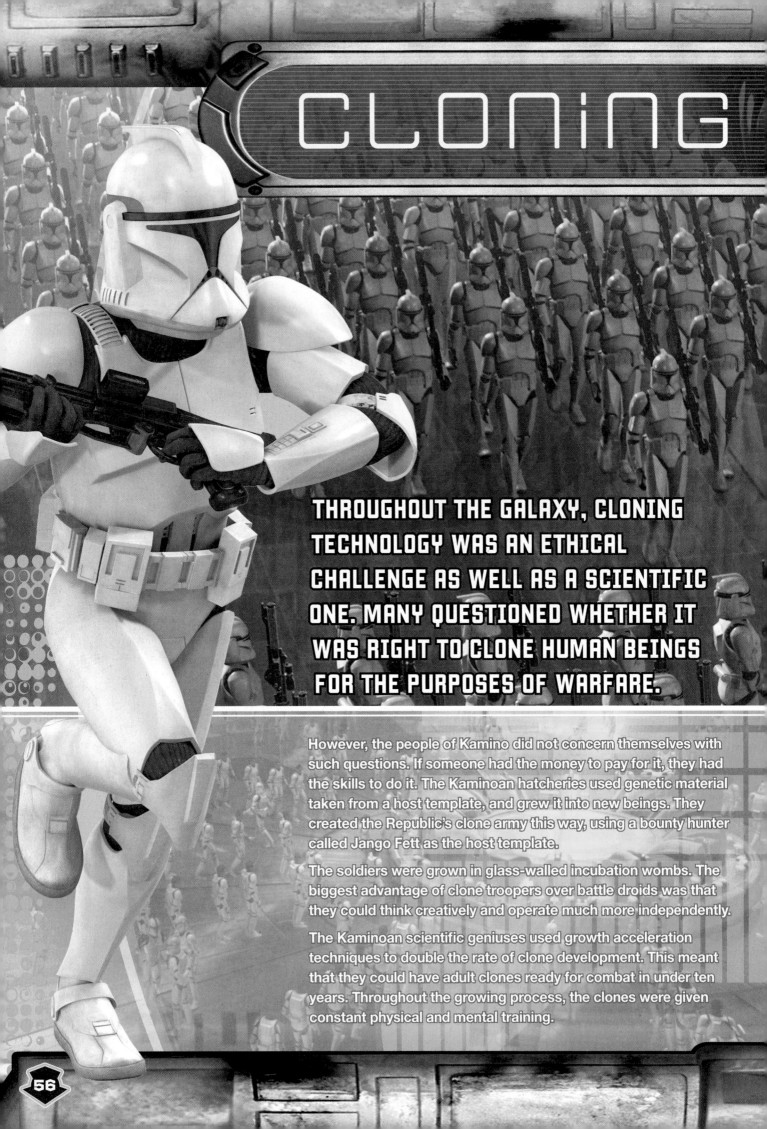

THROUGHOUT THE GALAXY, CLONING TECHNOLOGY WAS AN ETHICAL CHALLENGE AS WELL AS A SCIENTIFIC ONE. MANY QUESTIONED WHETHER IT WAS RIGHT TO CLONE HUMAN BEINGS FOR THE PURPOSES OF WARFARE.

However, the people of Kamino did not concern themselves with such questions. If someone had the money to pay for it, they had the skills to do it. The Kaminoan hatcheries used genetic material taken from a host template, and grew it into new beings. They created the Republic's clone army this way, using a bounty hunter called Jango Fett as the host template.

The soldiers were grown in glass-walled incubation wombs. The biggest advantage of clone troopers over battle droids was that they could think creatively and operate much more independently.

The Kaminoan scientific geniuses used growth acceleration techniques to double the rate of clone development. This meant that they could have adult clones ready for combat in under ten years. Throughout the growing process, the clones were given constant physical and mental training.

TECHNOLOGY

Clones received intensive military training, using simulated landscapes in vast rooms on Kamino. These environments could be anything from desert terrain to snow-blasted mountains.

The Clone Military Education Complex was the biggest training centre on Kamino. It was dedicatewd to fulfilling the Republic contract, which was the largest cloning job the Kaminoans had ever taken on. Sections of the centre included the hatchery, classroom, commissary, barracks, and parade grounds.

Elsewhere in the galaxy, the planet Khomm used cloning as the standard method of reproduction. When they believed that they had achieved the perfect society, they froze their own evolution and started to produce clones of previous generations.

A NEW HOPE

The droids landed on Tatooine and were captured by Jawas. The little scavengers sold them to Owen Lars and his nephew Luke.

Nineteen years after the Galactic Republic crumbled, Rebel spies stole secret plans to the Empire's ultimate weapon, the Death Star. Princess Leia of Alderaan had the plans, but Darth Vader boarded her starship. She had just enough time to give the plans to R2-D2, who escaped with C-3PO.

When Luke was cleaning R2-D2, he dislodged part of a hidden holo-message from Princess Leia, begging Obi-Wan Kenobi for help.

Before he could find the whole message, R2-D2 escaped and went to find Obi-Wan Kenobi. The former Jedi Master had been living as a hermit in the desert. Luke and C-3PO followed, and Luke found out that his father had once been a Jedi Knight. Obi-Wan gave Luke his father's lightsaber and told him about the Force.

Obi-Wan heard the message from the Princess, and asked Luke to go to Alderaan with him. At first Luke refused, but when Stormtroopers murdered his aunt and uncle, he agreed to join Obi-Wan on his mission.

At Mos Eisley spaceport, Obi-Wan hired Han Solo and Chewbacca to take them to Alderaan on Han's *Millennium Falcon*. Han owed money to Jabba the Hutt, so he was keen to get away from the planet.

7

In the skies above Alderaan, the Death Star arrived with Princess Leia aboard. Grand Moff Tarkin made her watch her home planet being destroyed. Then the *Millennium Falcon* arrived and was pulled on board the destroyer.

8

Han, Luke and Chewbacca went to rescue Princess Leia, while Obi-Wan set off to deactivate the tractor beam that was holding them. But Darth Vader sensed Obi-Wan's presence, and went to look for him.

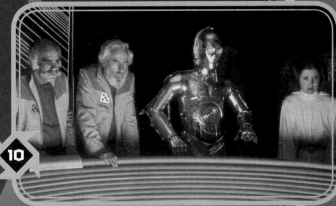

9

10

While the others were escaping, the two Jedi duelled for the second time. But as soon as he knew his friends were safe, Obi-Wan held up his lightsaber and allowed Darth Vader to kill him. Strangely, his body vanished when he died.

The *Millennium Falcon* escaped, but Darth Vader followed it to the Rebel headquarters on Yavin 4. The Rebels had to fight, and they had one advantage. The stolen plans showed them that one shot on a small thermal exhaust port could destroy the whole battle station.

11

12

Luke joined the Rebel pilots and flew towards the target. So far no one had been able to hit the thermal port, but he turned off his targeting computer and used the Force to aim.

Darth Vader was hot on his tail, but Vader could sense that the Force was strong with Luke. Then the *Millennium Falcon* appeared above him! Han attacked Darth Vader's TIE fighter and sent it spinning out of control. At the same time, Luke hit the target and the Death Star was destroyed. The Rebels had won their first victory!

KNOW YOUR ENEMY!

CAN YOU IDENTIFY THESE SHADY CHARACTERS FROM THE FRAGMENTS OF PHOTOGRAPHS? STUDY THE IMAGES AND WRITE THEIR NAMES BENEATH THE PICTURES.

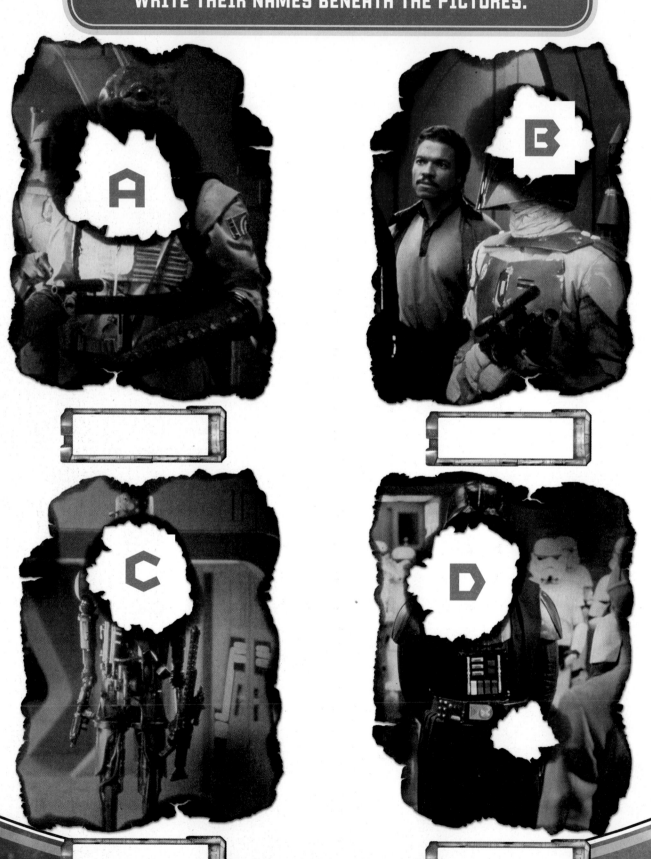

A

B

C

D

WORDSEARCH

ON GEONOSIS, ANAKIN, PADMÉ AND OBI-WAN ARE FIGHTING FOR THEIR LIVES! THERE ARE FIFTEEN WORDS CONNECTED WITH THEIR BATTLE IN THE ARENA OF GEONOSIS. CAN YOU FIND THEM ALL? THEY MAY BE WRITTEN FORWARDS, BACKWARDS, UP, DOWN OR DIAGONALLY.

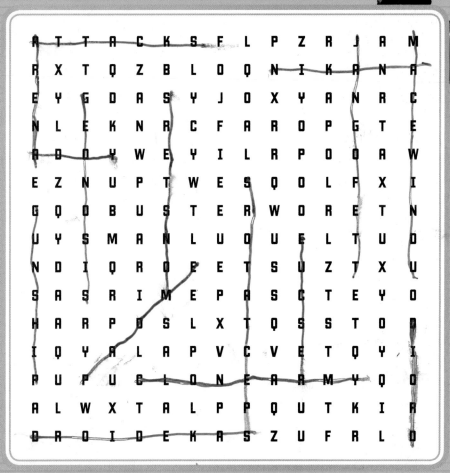

```
A T T A C K S F L P Z R J A M
R X T Q Z B L O Q N I K A N A
E Y G D A S Y J O X Y A N R C
N L E K N C F A R O P G T E
A D O Y W E Y I L R P O O A W
E Z N U P T W E S Q O L F X I
G Q O B U S T E R W O R E T N
U Y S M A N L U Q U E L T U D
N D I Q R O B E T S U Z T X U
S A S R I M E P A S C T E Y O
H A R P O S L X T Q S S T O D
I Q Y A L A P V C V E T Q Y I
P U P U C L O N E A R M Y Q O
A L W X T A L P P Q U T K I R
D R O I D E K A S Z U F R L O
```

- ✓ ARENA
- ✓ GEONOSIS
- ✓ RESCUE
- ✓ MONSTERS
- ✓ PADME
- ✓ SPECTATORS
- ✓ ATTACK
- ✓ MACE WINDU
- ✓ DROID
- ✓ JANGO FETT
- ✓ GUNSHIP
- ✓ CLONE ARMY
- ✓ ANAKIN
- ✓ YODA
- ✓ DROIDEKAS

TEMPLE ARCHITECT

THE JEDI TEMPLE ON CORUSCANT IS THE HEADQUARTERS OF THE JEDI ORDER. HERE, THE JEDI LIVE, TRAIN AND LEARN. IT IS A SACRED PLACE OF PEACE AND BEAUTY WITH ROOMS DEVOTED TO LEARNING AND MEDITATION.

IMAGINE THAT YOU ARE ESTABLISHING A NEW ORDER.

WHAT WOULD YOUR TEMPLE LOOK LIKE?

MAKE SURE THAT IT WILL BE SEEN FROM MILES AROUND.

POLITICIANS

SENATOR AMIDALA

Once the Queen of Naboo, Padmé Amidala became a Senator when she finished her term as ruler. She was much loved by the people she represented.

Padmé was passionate about public service from an early age. She joined the Apprentice Legislature at the age of eight and became an Apprentice Legislator when she was eleven.

The law of Naboo meant that Padmé had to step down as Queen after she had served her term, although the public loved her so much that they would have backed a change to the law. She could have retired at that point, but she was eager to work for the common good.

Padmé was outspoken and honest, and her wisdom was greatly admired. She was one of the few Senators who believed in a peaceful solution to the Separatist crisis, and for this reason her life was in great danger in the time leading up to the start of the Clone Wars.

SUPREME CHANCELLOR PALPATINE

In the early days of the Separatist crisis, Palpatine kept assuring the Senate that his main objective was peace, and that he would negotiate with the Separatists to achieve that.

However, everything changed when an assassin tried to take Senator Amidala's life. While she was in hiding, the Senate passed the Military Creation Act and gave Palpatine absolute power to commission an emergency army. His first act was to use the clone army that Obi-Wan had discovered.

Palpatine did not seem to take a strong position in any situation, and he was always careful to portray himself as a servant of the public good. He cultivated a gentle, quiet manner that cleverly disguised his ravenous ambition and ruthless intentions.

Outwardly, Palpatine always seemed to be working in the best interests of the Republic. But in the name of democracy he somehow managed to increase his own power, including the creation of the Chancellor's Red Guard. These bodyguards attended every committee meeting, and their training was kept secret. Behind the scenes, Palpatine was orchestrating every move like a puppet master. The last days of the Republic were getting closer and closer.

SENATOR ORGANA

Senator Bail Organa of Alderaan was a trusted advisor in Chancellor Palpatine's inner circle. He was a noble, honest and compassionate man, and a wise diplomat.

He was very compassionate and often spoke out in defence of the downtrodden. Like Senator Amidala, he did not believe that the clone army was the best way to meet the Separatist threat.

THE EMPIRE STRIKES BACK

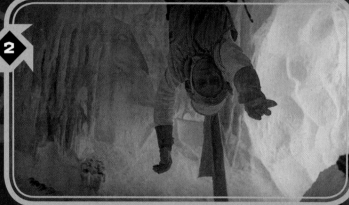

1

2

The Rebel Alliance suffered the fury of the Empire after their success at the Battle of Yavin. The Emperor wanted to wipe them out, and they were in hiding on the ice world of Hoth.

While Luke was out of the base, he spotted one of Darth Vader's Imperial probes. Before he could investigate, he was attacked by a Wampa and dragged to its cave. The probe let Darth Vader know that at last the Rebel base had been found.

3

4

Luke escaped from the Wampa's cave, but he was injured and freezing cold. Eventually he collapsed in the snow and had a vision of Obi-Wan Kenobi. The old Jedi told him to go to the Dagobah system and find Yoda. Han Solo found Luke unconscious in the snow. Eventually, they were able to return to the base.

The Rebels' sensors warned them that Darth Vader was coming. They started to evacuate the base, but they were not fast enough. Darth Vader arrived and sent his troops to the surface. A blood-curdling battle began.

5

6

Luke managed to destroy their walkers, giving his friends enough time to escape. The Rebels suffered terrible losses at the Battle of Hoth, but it could have been much worse.

When he was sure that his friends were safe, Luke headed for the Dagobah system with R2-D2. He met Yoda and started to learn how to be a Jedi. It was incredibly hard work, but he was determined to succeed.

Han, Chewbacca, Princess Leia and C-3PO flew to a nearby mining colony run by a friend of Han's, Lando Calrissian. They didn't know that the bounty hunter Boba Fett was following them.

Lando betrayed Han to Darth Vader to save his people. Han was frozen solid in carbonite and sent to Jabba the Hutt. On Dagobah, Luke's training was interrupted by a terrible vision of his friends in danger. Yoda could not stop him from going to rescue them and leaving his training unfinished.

Darth Vader was waiting for Luke. They duelled, but Luke was no match for Darth Vader's skill and experience. The Sith Lord cut off his opponent's hand before revealing that he was Luke's father.

Lando was not a bad man, and he felt guilty about betraying Han. He released Leia, C-3PO, R2-D2 and Chewbacca, and they all escaped in the *Millennium Falcon*.

Darth Vader tried to turn Luke to the dark side, but his son was strong and would not listen. He rolled himself off the high edge of the platform where they had been fighting and fell onto a metal frame below.

Luke hung on to the frame and cried out for Leia. Amazingly, she heard him and forced Lando to turn back. She knew that Luke needed her, and she rescued him and took him to safety. The Empire had flexed its muscles, and the Rebel Alliance had suffered a terrible blow.

ANIMALS OF THE GALAXY

WHAT SORT OF ANIMAL MIGHT YOU COME ACROSS ON THE ICY PLANET OF HOTH, OR THE DESERT PLANET OF TATOOINE. TEST YOUR KNOWLEDGE AND MATCH EACH PICTURE TO THE CORRECT NAME AND DESCRIPTION.

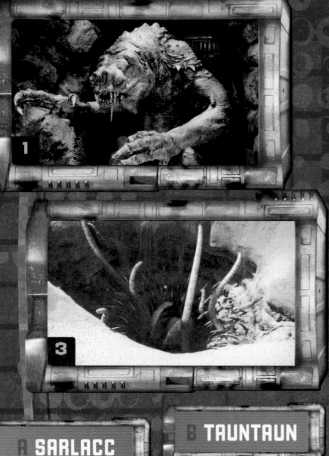

A SARLACC

B TAUNTAUN

C BANTHA

D RANCOR

YOUR ANSWERS...

PIC	NAME	DESC
1		III
2		I
3		II
4		IV

I | Placid, domesticated animals between 2 and 3 metres tall. They are strong, with long shaggy fur, and can survive in almost any environment.

II | Sharp teeth, a beak and long tentacles are all that can be seen of this fearsome animal. It can be found buried deep in the sands of Tatooine.

III | A favourite of Jabba the Hutt, this terrifying animal comes from the planet of Dathomir and grows up to 10 metres high. It has long arms and claws.

IV | Up to 3 metres tall, this vicious creature's shaggy white fur protects it from the ice and snow of Hoth.

CROSS WORD

1 | Han Solo's ship

2 | Luke Skywalker's twin sister

3 | Luke is chased by this furry creature on the icy planet of Hoth

4 | Han Solo's Wookiee first mate

5 | Obi-Wan Kenobi instructs Luke to train under Jedi _____ Yoda

6 | Luke Skywalker's weapon

7 | Ruthless gangster who has a bounty on Han Solo

8 | To escape the Imperial Fleet, the *Millennium Falcon* hides in an _____ field

9 | Darth Vader is Luke's _____

10 | The planet run by Han Solo's friend Lando Calrissian

M
I
L L E I A
L   W
L   K
E   M
N   P
I   A
U   FATHER
M A S T E R   A
F   T
A   H
L I G H T S A B E R
C
O
N

NEW Clone Trooper

THE KAMINOANS HAVE CREATED A NEW BATTALION OF CLONES TO PROTECT THE REPUBLIC.

THE ARMY IS ALMOST COMPLETE, BUT CHANCELLOR PALPATINE HAS ASKED YOU TO DESIGN A NEW UNIFORM FOR THE CLONE TROOPERS.

ARE YOU UP TO THE CHALLENGE

MATCH THE PAIRS

HOW WELL DO YOU KNOW YOUR HEROES AND VILLAINS? WHERE DO THESE IMPORTANT CHARACTERS COME FROM? CAN YOU MATCH EACH ONE TO THEIR HOME PLANET?

PADMÉ

LAMA SU

GEONOSIS

NABOO

KAMINO

ANAKIN

POGGLE
THE LESSER

TATOOINE

GEONOSIAN factories

WHEN OBI-WAN KENOBI, PADMÉ AMIDALA AND ANAKIN SKYWALKER ARRIVED ON GEONOSIS, THEY DISCOVERED MASSIVE UNDERGROUND FACTORIES THAT WERE BUSILY MAKING THOUSANDS OF BATTLE DROIDS.

The Geonosians were hard-working, and they poured their energy into the creation of a Separatist army. They used advanced technology in the service of the Techno Union as well as other commerce guilds.

Baktoid Armor Workshop was a key technology developer in the Techo Union, and at one time they had factories throughout the galaxy. However, as laws were tightened they were forced to rethink their strategy. They closed down factories throughout the Inner Rim and Colonies regions, including Foundry, Ord Cestus, Telti, Balmorra and Ord Lithone. Later they moved their operations beyond the jurisdiction of the Republic, concentrating on Outer Rim planets like Geonosis.

The corporation explained away their continued purchase of raw materials as investment for the future, but the truth was that they were building an army away from the prying eyes of the Republic. Anyone who was sent to investigate mysteriously disappeared.

The larger factories were mostly automated, with frighteningly gigantic conveyer belts and robot arms that put mechanical pieces together. Battalions of battle droids, super battle droids and droidekas were built beneath the red surface of Geonosis.

RETURN OF THE JEDI

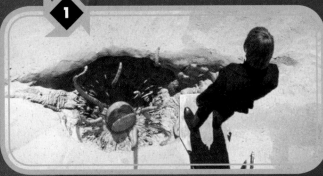

1

2

Han Solo was hanging on Jabba the Hutt's wall like a picture, frozen in carbonite. His friends went to his rescue, but they were caught red-handed. Jabba the Hutt took them to the Great Pit of Carkoon to feed them to the Sarlacc. However, his triumph was short-lived. He died at the hands of Princess Leia and the friends returned to help the Rebel Alliance.

Luke returned to Yoda to complete his training, but he was only just in time to say goodbye as the old Master died. His body vanished as he became one with the Force.

In a vision, Obi-Wan told Luke that Princess Leia was his twin sister. He added that Luke would have to kill Darth Vader. But Luke refused to kill his own father.

3

4

The Emperor had commissioned a new Death Star, and the Rebels knew that it would destroy them. They had to destroy it before it was completed. However, the Emperor and Darth Vader were plotting to turn Luke to the dark side.

The Rebels planned to deactivate the Death Star's energy shield from the forest moon of Endor. When the shield was down, they could destroy the battle station. Han was in charge of the strike team, which included Luke, Leia and Chewbacca. Lando would lead the attack on the Death Star.

5

6

On Endor, the strike team met a tribe of Ewoks and made friends with them. Luke told Leia that he was her brother. He also realised that Darth Vader knew he was there. To protect his friends, he surrendered to Darth Vader.

Luke tried to talk to Anakin Skywalker. He believed that there was still good in his father. But the Emperor had controlled Darth Vader for too long, and Luke could not make him turn away from the dark side.

On board the Death Star, Luke came face to face with the Emperor. He was shocked to find out that his enemy knew all about the Rebel attack. It was a trap!

On Endor, the strike team was captured by Stormtroopers. The Alliance fighters came out of hyperspace while the shield was still working. Luke watched the battle between the Rebels and the Imperial fighters.

The Emperor tried to force Luke to turn to the dark side, but he resisted. On Endor, the Ewoks came to the rescue and freed Han and Leia. They deactivated the shield generator just in time.

In a moment of weakness, Luke gave in to his anger and fought his father. However, his goodness was stronger and he refused to fight any more. The Emperor attacked him with Force lightning, ready to destroy him.

At the last second, Darth Vader knew that he couldn't let the Emperor kill his son. He became Anakin Skywalker again, and sacrificed himself to throw his Sith Master down the power shaft. Luke held Anakin in his arms and comforted him as his father took his final breaths. Then, as the Death Star started to explode, Luke escaped in a small fighter.

The galaxy celebrated the end of the Empire, and a new Republic was born. The old prophecy had come true at last. The Chosen One had restored balance to the Force.

WORD PYRAMID

CAN YOU THINK LOGICALLY EVEN UNDER PRESSURE? TEST YOUR PROBLEM SOLVING SKILLS BY COMPLETING THIS WORD PUZZLE.

START WITH THE LETTER A AND ADD ONE LETTER AT A TIME BY ANSWERING THE CLUES.

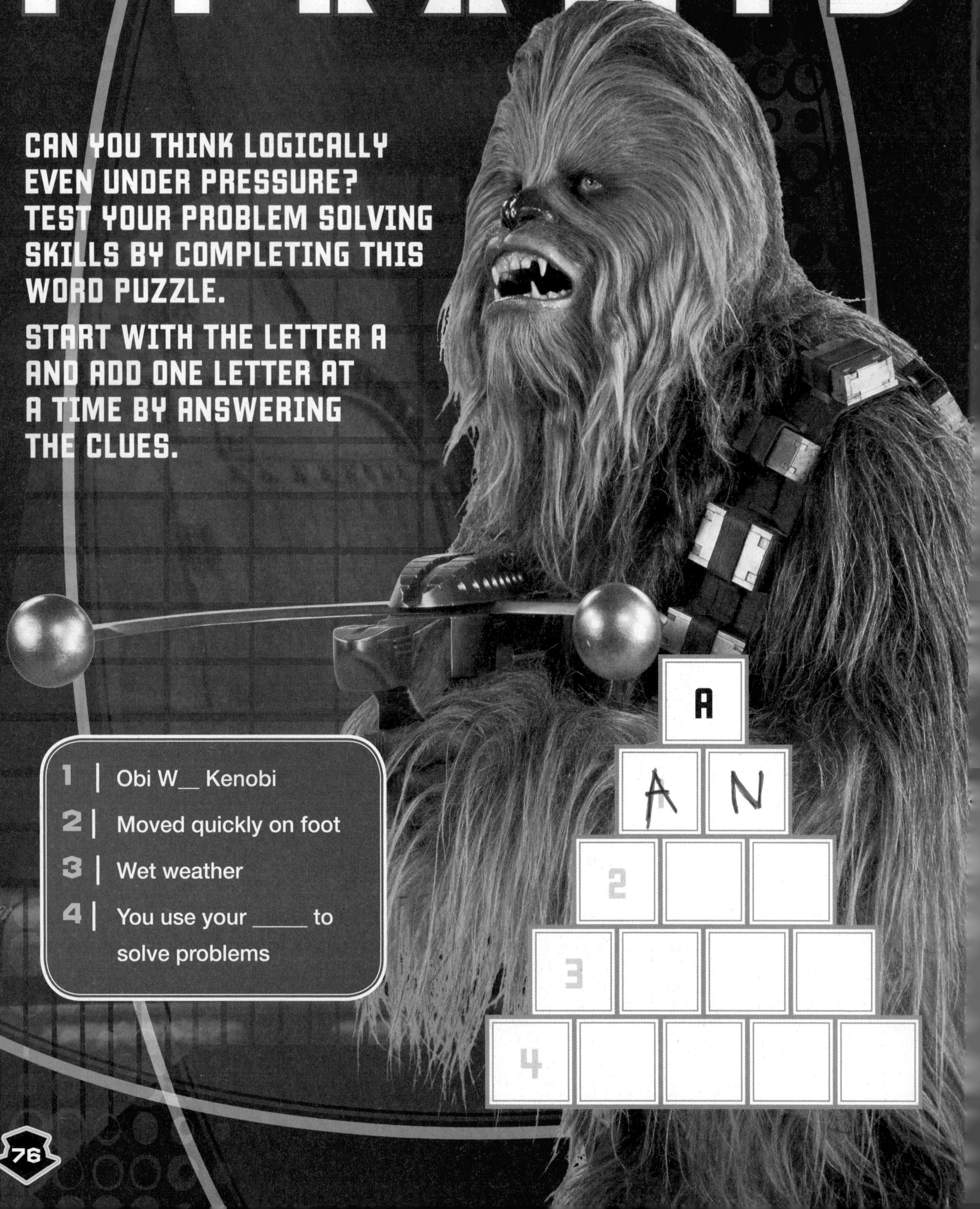

1	Obi W__ Kenobi
2	Moved quickly on foot
3	Wet weather
4	You use your _____ to solve problems

A

A N

2

3

4

SPOT THE DIFFERENCE

OBSERVATION SKILLS ARE AN IMPORTANT PART OF YOUR JEDI TRAINING. THERE ARE 10 DIFFERENCES BETWEEN THESE TWO PICTURES. CAN YOU FIND THEM ALL?

ANSWERS

PAGE 12 - ODD ONE OUT

Picture 5

PAGE 13 - WORD WISDOM

1 | Naboo
2 | Jar Jar Binks
3 | Darth Maul
4 | Anakin Skywalker
5 | Senator Palpatine
6 | Tatooine

PAGE 19 - TOOLS OF THE TRADE

RETRACTABLE WRIST BLADES

BLASTER RIFLE

DUAL BLASTER PISTOLS

SNARE ROCKET DARTS

FLAME PROJECTOR

VIBROBLADE

PAGE 22-23 - BATTLE CHALLENGE

Nute Gunray | Rune Haako | Darth Sidious
Count Dooku | Poggle the Lesser | Jango Fett

PAGE 42 - SHADOW SEARCHER

A | Boba Fett
B | Anakin
C | Poggle
D | Yoda
E | Droid
F | Padmé Amidala

PAGE 43 - JEDI PROPHECY

Senator Padmé Amidala is in danger! An attempt will be made on her life. The assassin will tell you nothing, but a clue could lead you to the ocean planet of Kamino. There you will find a secret army hidden by the Republic.

There are challenges ahead, young Jedi. Your quest will lead you to the desert planet of Geonosis, where you will find great danger awaits you! A former Jedi will try to tempt you. You must remain strong. The Jedi Council must be told of the droid army before it is too late.

PAGE 53 - SUDOKU

5	7	9	1	6	3	8	2	1
8	4	3	2	9	7	5	6	1
2	1	6	5	8	4	3	9	7
4	6	8	9	2	5	7	1	3
1	2	7	6	3	8	9	4	5
3	9	5	7	4	1	2	8	6
6	3	4	8	7	2	1	5	9
9	8	1	3	5	6	4	7	2
7	5	2	4	1	9	6	3	8

PAGE 55 - FACT OR FICTION

1 | False
2 | True
3 | False
4 | True
5 | True
6 | True
7 | False
8 | True
9 | False
10 | False

PAGE 60 - KNOW YOUR ENEMY

A | Bossk
B | Boba Fett
C | IG-88
D | Darth Vader

PAGE 61 - WORDSEARCH

PAGE 68 - ANIMALS OF THE GALAXY

1 | D - Rancor - III
2 | C - Bantha - I
3 | A - Sarlacc - II
4 | B - Tauntaun - IV

PAGE 69 - CROSSWORD

PAGE 71 - MATCH THE PAIRS

Padmé Amidala | Naboo
Anakin Skywalker | Tatooine
Lama Su | Kamino
Poggle the Lesser | Geonosis

PAGE 76 - WORD PYRAMID

A
A N
R A N
R A I N
B R A I N

PAGE 77 - SPOT THE DIFFERENCE